BLACKWELL HABITAT FIELD GUIDES

Herbaceous Flowering Aquatic Plants

Michael Quigley

*Senior Lecturer in Environmental Biology,
Nene College, Northampton*

Basil Blackwell

An Introduction to the Habitat Keys

The series of selected habitat keys for flowering plants has been designed for the beginner in field studies and any other interested person. It is hoped that the keys will provide a straightforward method of identifying the more common flowering plants which occur in the habitats considered.

There is inevitably a flaw in this approach that the user should bear in mind. Since only the more commonly occurring plants are included, it is possible that you will encounter plants which are not mentioned in the keys. It is important that you do not attempt to make a particular plant fit one of the descriptions given. Should you wish to identify plants not considered in the keys, it is suggested that you refer to the bibliography for suitable references. For most purposes *The Wild Flower Key*, Francis Rose, is highly recommended.

How to use the keys

Before you attempt to identify a plant, familiarise yourself with the lay-out of the keys. Scientific and common names are given for all the plants considered in each key. Line diagrams are also provided in the hope that they will support the written descriptions. Do not rely on the diagrams alone to identify the plant. Use the glossary provided to obtain descriptions of terms used in the keys which are unfamiliar to you.

Always work through the key in a systematic manner using the instructions given below. Do not attempt to make a plant fit a particular description. The plant in question may not be in the keys.

1 On the left-hand side of each page are numbers arranged in sequence. (The numbers in brackets beside them will enable you to retrace your identification if you feel that you have made a mistake.) Each number is set against a pair of contrasting statements **a** and **b**. (Occasionally, a third statement **c** is given.)

One of these statements should provide a partial description of the plant you wish to identify. Examine each plant carefully, using a 10x hand lens where necessary to provide details of the structure. Then study each statement and decide which most closely describes your specimen.

2 Each statement ends *either* in an arrow pointing to a number *or* in a box naming a plant. If the statement ends in an arrow, this means 'go on to' the number indicated. Find this number on the left-hand side of a page and continue your identification until a statement ends by naming a plant. At this point the identification is complete.

Glossary

achene	a small nut-like fruit
acute	a sharp angle, less than a right-angle
alternate	leaves alternating up the stem — first on one side and then on the other
anther	see **flower**
awn	a stiff, bristle-like projection arising from the spikelets of grasses
axis	main stem running through an inflorescence
basal	leaves at the base of the stem at ground level
bract	a leaf with a flower in its axil
bracteole	a tiny leaf on a flower-stem without a flower in its axil
bristle-like (leaves)	tightly rolled and appearing like a bristle
calyx	see **flower**
capsule	dry fruit that opens into two or more parts or by a lid or holes to release seeds
catkin	a spike of minute flowers, male and female borne separately
compound	a leaf divided into distinct, separate leaflets

trifoliate   palmate   1-pinnate   2-pinnate   3-pinnate

converging	tendency to meet at a point
corolla	see **flower**
corymb	an inflorescence with the outer flower-stalks much longer than the inner ones. The flowers are at roughly the same level in a flat-topped cluster
cyme	an inflorescence in which the top flowers open first. Lower flowers open in sequence lowest opening last
deciduous	a woody plant which loses its leaves in the autumn
disc	see **florets**
diverging	tendency to spread from a point

alternate

awn

bract

catkin

corymb

cyme

2

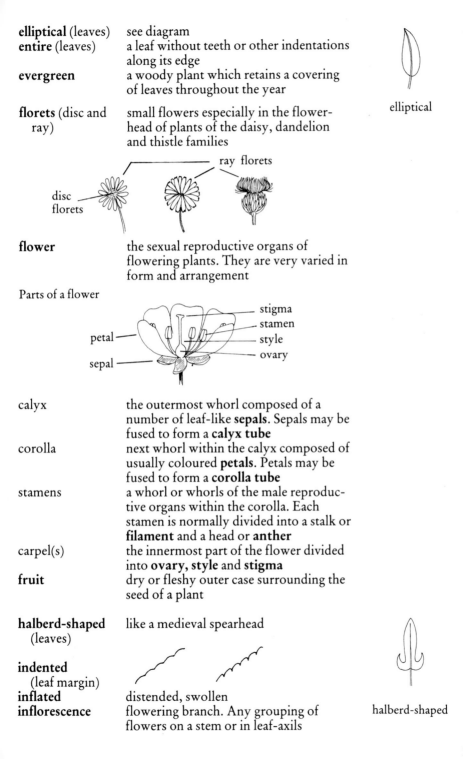

elliptical (leaves)	see diagram
entire (leaves)	a leaf without teeth or other indentations along its edge
evergreen	a woody plant which retains a covering of leaves throughout the year
florets (disc and ray)	small flowers especially in the flower-head of plants of the daisy, dandelion and thistle families

elliptical

ray florets

disc florets

flower	the sexual reproductive organs of flowering plants. They are very varied in form and arrangement

Parts of a flower

stigma
stamen
petal
style
ovary
sepal

calyx	the outermost whorl composed of a number of leaf-like **sepals**. Sepals may be fused to form a **calyx tube**
corolla	next whorl within the calyx composed of usually coloured **petals**. Petals may be fused to form a **corolla tube**
stamens	a whorl or whorls of the male reproductive organs within the corolla. Each stamen is normally divided into a stalk or **filament** and a head or **anther**
carpel(s)	the innermost part of the flower divided into **ovary, style** and **stigma**
fruit	dry or fleshy outer case surrounding the seed of a plant
halberd-shaped (leaves)	like a medieval spearhead
indented (leaf margin)	
inflated	distended, swollen
inflorescence	flowering branch. Any grouping of flowers on a stem or in leaf-axils

halberd-shaped

3

lanceolate (leaves)	lance-shaped	lanceolate
leaflets	the separate leaf-blades of a compound leaf	
ligule(s) (in grasses)	a small flap of tissue or fringe of hairs where the leaf-blade joins its sheathing base	
linear (leaves)	long, narrow, more or less parallel-sided leaf	
lyre shaped (leaves)	see diagram	

lyre-shaped

ligule   leaf-blade

membranous (ligules)	a flap of tissue
midrib	the main, central vein of a leaf
oblong (leaves)	a leaf about two or three times as long as broad, parallel sided in the central part
oval, ovate (leaves)	rather egg shaped, about twice as long as broad
opposite (leaves)	leaves arising in pairs

oblong   oval

opposite

palmate	see **compound**
panicle	a branched raceme (see **raceme**)
pendulous	hanging down
pinnatifid (leaves)	a deeply cut leaf but not cut right to midrib
pinnate (1, 2 or 3)	see **compound**
prickles	a sharp, usually curved, outgrowth from the outer layers
prostrate	lying in a horizontal position

pinnatifid

raceme	a more or less elongated inflorescence in which the lowest flower opens first, and then the others open in sequence towards the tip
rhizome	a creeping, underground stem
root-leaves	leaves arranged at the stem base at ground level

raceme   panicle

rosette (of leaves)	leaves arranged in a more or less flat position to the ground	
runner	a creeping stem above the ground, can root at tip to form a new plant	

rosette

sepals	see **flower**
sessile	without a stalk
sheath	lower part of the leaf surrounding a stem
shrub	a woody plant without a main trunk, branched from the base
simple (leaves)	not divided into leaflets, margin may be entire, lobed or toothed
spike	an unbranched flower-head
spikelet	unit of a grass flower-head
spike-like	resembling a spike
spine	a stiff straight sharp-pointed structure
spur (in flowers)	a cylindrical or conical, sometimes curved, hollow projection from the back of certain flowers
stamens	see **flower**
stigma	see **flower**
stipules	leaf-like or scale-like structures at the base of the leaf-stalk or stem
stolon	a creeping stem above ground, not necessarily rooting at tip
strap-shaped	flat, parallel-sided, blunt-tipped leaf

simple leaf   spike

spikelets

stipules

terminal	at the tip
thorn	a woody sharp-pointed structure
tree	a woody plant with a main trunk
trifoliate	see **compound**
tufted	loose, compact or dense cluster
tussock	a clump

umbel	a flat-topped inflorescence with several branches all arising from one point at the top of the main stem, may be simple or compound
umbel-like	like an umbel inflorescence

umbel

whorl	more than two structures (e.g. leaves) of the same kind arising at the same level

whorl

Some Common Herbaceous Flowering Aquatic Plants

The flowering plants considered in this key may be found in or near lakes, ponds, rivers and streams, or wet meadows and fens. The key may also be of use in identifying the flowering plants of dune slacks.

Use the information given below to determine the group to which your plant belongs and proceed to the section indicated by one of the letters A, B, C or D. (Use the glossary if you do not understand any of the terms used in the key.)

1 Leaves **narrow linear: grass-like**, long **strap-like** or **sword-like**, or **cylindrical**. Some plants apparently **without leaves** or leaves reduced to **scales** at the base of cylindrical stems.

> SECTION A
> Pages 7–14

2 Plant of **open water** with **floating** and/or **submerged** leaves only; no aerial leaves. (Flower-stalks may rise above the water surface.)

> SECTION B
> Pages 15–22

3 Leaves **simple**, variously arranged; some plants in water but with aerial leaves and flowers.

> SECTION C
> Pages 23–33

4 Leaves **pinnatifid** or **compound**.

> SECTION D
> Pages 34–40

SECTION A

1 **a** Plant **rush-like**; apparently **without leaves** or leaves reduced to **scales** at the bases of cylindrical stems. ──────────────────▶ 2

    b Plant with **distinct leaves**. ──────────────────▶ 5

2 (1) **a** Inflorescences **terminal**. ──────────────────▶ 3

       b Inflorescences from **side of stems**. ──────────────▶ 4

3 (2) **a** Stems **stout**; more than 1 cm across; 1–3 m tall. Stem interior spongy. Flower-heads egg-shaped; spikelets reddish brown.

> *Scirpus lacustris*
> Bulrush

       b Stems **far-creeping**; 10–60 cm tall; solitary or in tufts. Inflorescence solitary; red-brown; cigar-shaped spikes.

> *Eleocharis palustris*
> Common Spike Rush

4 (2) **a** Stems erect and tufted; stiff; **strongly ridged**; 2–3 mm thick; contains white spongy pith. Bright green to yellowish green. Inflorescences from side of stem some way below tip; compact; densely branched; dark reddish.

> *Juncus conglomeratus*
> Common Rush

       b Differs from **a** in that the stems are **smooth** and **scarcely ridged**. Inflorescence may be loose or condensed.

> *Juncus effusus*
> Soft Rush

5 (1) **a** Leaves **linear** and mostly basal; 10–20 cm long; rounded on lower side and deeply grooved on upper side. Plant slender; erect; aromatic smell when bruised. Inflorescence a raceme of many small and greenish flowers.

> *Triglochin palustre*
> Marsh Arrowgrass

b Leaves large, **strap-** or **sword-shaped**; either flattened in one plane or broadside on to stems. ⟶ 6
c Leaves **grass-like** or **cylindrical**. Flowers small, usually clustered; individually inconspicuous. ⟶ 11

6 (5) **a** Leaves **sword-like**; flattened in one plane; **iris-like**. Plant 40–130 cm tall. Flowers yellow; iris-like; 8–10 cm across.

> *Iris pseudocorus*
> Yellow Iris

b Leaves **strap-like**, broadside on to the stems. ⟶ 7

7 (6) **a** Leaves **basal only**. ⟶ 8
b Leaves **basal** and **alternating** up the stems. ⟶ 10

8 (7) **a** Leaves three-angled, twisted. Flowers many, in **umbels** of unequal stalks. Petals three; all rosy pink. Plant up to 1.5 m tall. Found in shallow water.

> *Butomus umbellatus*
> Flowering Rush

b Leaves strap-like, inflorescence a terminal, cigar-shaped, **brown spike**. ⟶ 9

9 (8) **a** Leaves 10–20 mm **wide**. Plant 1.5–2.5 m tall.

> *Typha latifolia*
> Common Reedmace

b As tall as **a** above but more **slender**.
Leaves only 4–5 mm wide.

> *Typha angustifolia*
> Lesser Reedmace

10 (7) **a** Plant erect; 50–150 cm tall. Inflorescence
stems **branched** bearing spiked, ball-like
flowers. Male flowers above female flowers.

> *Sparganium erectum*
> Branched Bur-Reed

b Plant similar to **a** but only 20–60 cm tall
and inflorescence stems **not branched**.

> *Sparganium emersum*
> Unbranched Bur-Reed

11 (5) **a** Leaves **cylindrical**; hairless. Stems not angled; inflorescence terminal. Leaves up the stem pointed, with **internal cross-partitions** (open the leaf with your thumbnail). Inflorescence much branched and loose.

> *Juncus articulatus*
> Jointed Rush

b Leaves in two vertical ranks. Stems hollow and round. ──────▶ 12
c Leaves hairless; in three vertical ranks along the stems. Stems often three-angled. Male and female flowers usually on separate, dissimilar spikes on the same stem. ────────────────────▶ 18

12 (11) **a** Ligules a **dense fringe** of hairs. Plant 1.5–3 m tall. Leaves grey-green; up to 60 cm long; blades long, tapering to fine, curved tip. Inflorescences erect or finally nodding; 15–40 cm long; loose to dense; soft; may be purplish or brownish.

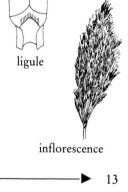

ligule

> *Phragmites communis*
> Common Reed

inflorescence

b Ligules **membranous**. ────────────────────▶ 13

13 (12) **a** Ligules **spike-like** or **pointed**; up to 15 mm long. ──────▶ 14
b Ligules **blunt**; may become torn. ──────────────▶ 15

14 (13) a Ligules **spike-like**; up to 15 mm long. Grasses 20–200 cm tall, forming large tussocks. Leaves hairless, green; blades somewhat blunt or sharply pointed; sheaths rounded on the back; stiff and rough. Inflorescences open, loose; erect or nodding; 10–50 cm long and up to 20 cm wide. Spikelets loosely scattered; lanceolate to narrow oblong.

Deschampsia caespitosa
Tufted Hair Grass

b Ligules **pointed**; 5–15 mm long. Grass loosely tufted or forming loose masses in shallow water; up to 1 m tall. Leaves green, hairless; blade pointed; 5–25 cm long. Inflorescences open in flower; afterwards contracted and narrow. Branches in pairs or solitary; the longer of the pair bearing one to four spikelets. Spikelets narrow oblong; up to 36 mm long; greenish or purple.

Glyceria fluitans
Floating Sweet Grass

15 (13) a Inflorescences forming a very dense, narrowly cylindrical spike; up to 7 cm long. Ligules blunt; 2–5 mm long. Grasses sometimes extensively creeping with obvious nodes and an angular habit. Leaves hairless; blades pointed, flat; 2–12 cm long. Grass 15–45 cm tall.

Alopecurus geniculatus
Marsh Fox-tail

b Inflorescences dense or open; not spike-like. ———▶ 16

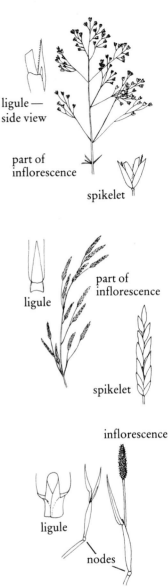

ligule —
side view

part of
inflorescence

spikelet

ligule

part of
inflorescence

spikelet

inflorescence

ligule

nodes

16 (15) **a** Inflorescences open and loose; ovate to oblong; 15–45 cm long; much branched. Branches very slender; rough; lower branches up to 20 cm long. Grass up to 2.5 m tall, spreading by rhizomes. Ligules 3–6 mm long, usually with a central point. Leaves green, hairless, with cross nerves; abruptly pointed; 30–60 cm long. Spikelets oblong; 6–15 mm long.

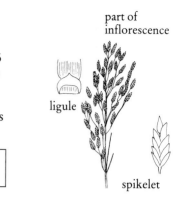

part of inflorescence

ligule

spikelet

> *Glyceria maxima*
> Reed Sweet Grass

b Inflorescences lanceolate, linear or oblong; spikelets clustered or crowded. ──────────────────────────▶ 17

17 (16) **a** Ligules blunt; 3–15 mm long; often torn. Grass 60–200 cm tall; spreading extensively by creeping rhizomes. Leaves finely pointed; 10–36 cm long; flat, firm, hairless; green or whitish green. Inflorescences lanceolate to oblong; dense or somewhat loose below; 5–25 cm long. Spikelets densely crowded; oblong or gaping.

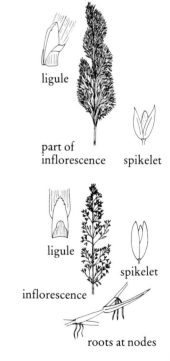

ligule

part of inflorescence   spikelet

> *Phalaris arundinacea*
> Reed Canary Grass

b Ligules blunt; 1–6 mm long. Grass extensively creeping; 8–40 cm tall; rooting from lower nodes. Leaves hairless; green, greyish or bluish green. Blades finely pointed; 1–10 cm long; rolled when young, flat when older. Inflorescences linear to lanceolate; 1–12 cm long; up to 3 cm wide.

ligule

inflorescence

spikelet

roots at nodes

> *Agrostis stolonifera*
> Creeping Bent

18 (11) **a** Stems shorter than leaves; three-angled above, more rounded below. Leaves 3–7 mm wide; often in-rolled; greyish. Plant 30–60 cm tall. Inflorescence of stalked, erect, sausage-shaped spikes; two-to-four male spikes; above two-to-four shortish, fat female spikes at intervals down stem. Lowest of leaf-like bracts equalling or overtopping the top spike.

> *Carex rostata*
> Bottle Sedge

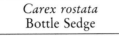

b Stems entirely sharply three-angled. ⟶ 19

c Stems not sharply angled; often smooth. ⟶ 21

19 (18) **a** Leaves **narrow**, 2–3 mm wide; greyish; sheaths at base soon decaying to black fibrous mass. Plant 7–70 cm tall. Inflorescence with one or two black male spikes (lower spikes usually smaller) above two or three rather short, sausage-shaped, female spikes on short stalks. Lowest leaf-like bract sometimes overtopping top spike.

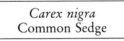

> *Carex nigra*
> Common Sedge

b Leaves **wider**, from 6 to 15 mm wide. ⟶ 20

20 (19) **a** Leaves 7–10 mm wide; broad keeled; all parts rough when rubbed downwards. Stem shorter than some leaves. Plant bluish grey; 60–150 cm tall. Inflorescence spikes long, fattish, two or three males close together above three or four more widely separated females. Lowest bracts leaf-like, overtopping the top spike.

> *Carex acutiformis*
> Lesser Pond Sedge

b Similar to **a** but leaves 6–15 mm wide. Plant 1–1.5 m tall; not bluish grey. Inflorescence with up to six male spikes; female spikes longer and on longer stalks; lowest female spikes drooping.

> *Carex riparia*
> Great Pond Sedge

21 (18) **a** Leaves 2–5 mm wide; greyish; sheaths **dull brown**. Plant 10–40 cm (sometimes 60 cm) tall. Inflorescence with single male spike (drooping when in fruit); one or two (sometimes three) female spikes, distant, erect. Lowest bract leaf-like; closely sheathing; shorter than top spike.

> *Carex panicea*
> Carnation Sedge

b Leaves 2–4 mm wide; greyish; sheaths **reddish**. Plant 10–40 cm tall with **creeping rootstock**. Inflorescence with one-to-three thin, erect male spikes and two long-stalked, fattish, drooping female spikes rather close together at the top of the stem. Bracts leaf-like, usually shorter than the top spike. Often confused with **a**.

> *Carex flacca*
> Glaucous Sedge

SECTION B

1   **a** Plant tiny; **oval** or **lanceolate-oblong**; free-floating, forming green carpets on water. ————————————————————▶ 2

    b Plant without the combined features of the above. ——————▶ 5

2   (1) **a** Plant **elliptical-lanceolate**; joined up at right-angles into branched colonies. Terminal triplets look like ivy leaves.

> *Lemna trisulca*
> Ivy-leaved Duckweed

    b Plant **oval**; roots **several** or **single**. ————————————————▶ 3

3   (2) **a** Plant with **several long roots**. Flat both sides; 5–8 mm across; often purple below.

> *Lemna polyrhiza*
> Greater Duckweed

    b Plant with **single root**. ——————————————————————▶ 4

4   (3) **a** **Flat** both sides; up to 4 mm across.

> *Lemna minor*
> Common Duckweed

    b **Convex above**; white spongy and **swollen below**. May produce attached daughter plants each with a single root.

> *Lemna gibba*
> Fat Duckweed

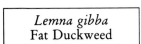

5 (1) **a** Plant with **round, heart- or kidney-shaped** floating leaves; like water-lilies. ──────────────► 6

    b Leaves of other shape, variously arranged. ──────────► 8

6 (5) **a** Leaves **round** or **kidney-shaped**; up to 3 cm across. Leaves long-stalked with large papery stipules. Flowers long-stalked; 2 cm across; arising from water. Petals, three; white, crinkly, with yellow spot at bases.

> *Hydrocharis*
> *morsus-ranae*
> Frogbit

    b Leaves normally over 10 cm across. ──────────────► 7

7 (6) **a** Leathery **heart-shaped** leaves on long elastic stalks. Some thinner submerged leaves. Flowers up to 6 cm across with about 20 yellow petals and many stamens.

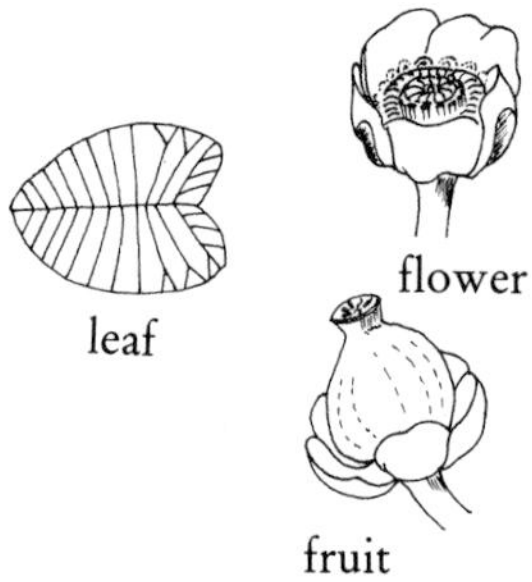

leaf

flower

> *Nuphar lutea*
> Yellow Water-Lily

fruit

    b Leaves **almost circular**. Flowers up to 20 cm across with 20–25 white petals.

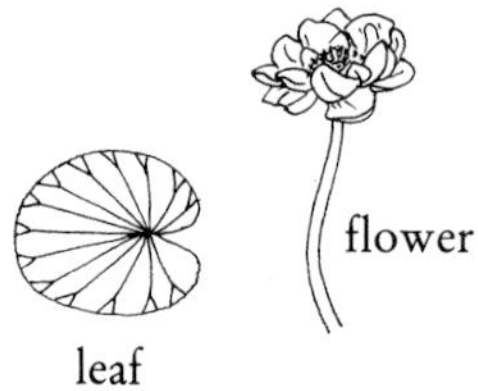

> *Nymphaea alba*
> White Water-Lily

flower

leaf

8 (5) **a** Leaves **alternate** (near opposite on flower-stalks of some species); stipules at bases. ──────────────▶ 9
   b Leaves of other arrangement. ──────────▶ 13

9 (8) **a** Floating leaves **oval** to **elliptical-lanceolate.** ─────────▶ 10
   b Leaves **narrow linear,** submerged. ─────────▶ 11

10 (9) **a** Leaves with **discoloured flexible joint** just below top of the narrow leaf-stalks. Floating leaves dark green; leathery; opaque; 10–30 cm long; pointed at tips and rounded at base. Submerged leaves narrow linear. Flower-spike dense; 3–8 cm long; emerging from the water.

leaf

| *Potamogeton natans* |
| Broad-leaved Pondweed |

   b Leaves similar to **a** but without discoloured flexible joint. Leaves often reddish-brown; floating leaves 6–10 cm long, tapering into stalk or heart-shaped base. Submerged leaves with translucent blades.

| *Potamogeton* |
| *polygonifolius* |
| Bog Pondweed |

11 (9) **a** Many leaves, each composed of two slender parallel tubes. Leaves 5–20 cm long to 2 mm wide. Inflorescence open and very loose; on long stalks.

| *Potamogeton pectinatus* |
| Fennel Pondweed |

   b Leaves not of two slender tubes. ──────────▶ 12

12 (11) **a** Leaves translucent; dark green; stalkless; toothed; three-to-five veins; blunt tipped. Stems four-angled; furrowed.

leaf

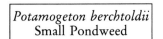

> *Potamogeton crispus*
> Curled Pondweed

b Leaves flat; up to 5 cm long; 2 mm wide. Three long veins; outer veins meet midrib nearly at right angles, half-to-one leaf width from sharp-pointed tip.

> *Potamogeton berchtoldii*
> Small Pondweed

leaf

13 (8) **a** Leaves **opposite**; in pairs. ⟶ 14
  b Leaves of other arrangement. ⟶ 17

14 (13) **a** Upper pairs of leaves close set and forming a flat, **floating rosette.** ⟶ 15
  b Upper pairs of leaves not forming a floating rosette. ⟶ 16

15 (14) **a** Leaves more or less oval, untoothed, with **shallow notch** at tips; leaf rosettes usually present. Roots arise from base of leaf pairs. Found in water, on wet mud etc.

> *Callitriche stagnalis*
> Common Water
> Starwort

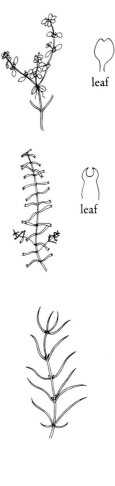

leaf

b Lower leaves linear with **deeply notched**, spanner-shaped tips. Upper leaves may be spoon-shaped or elliptical, or all leaves may be linear and parallel sided. Found in water, on wet mud etc.

> *Callitriche intermedia*
> Intermediate Water
> Starwort

leaf

16 (14) **a Stipules present** at leaf bases. Leaves linear; sometimes hair-like; up to 5 cm long; flat; fine-pointed; translucent. Much-branched slender shoots up to 50 cm long. Flowers tiny in more or less unstalked clusters in leaf-axils.

> *Zannichellia palustris*
> Horned Pondweed

b Stipules absent. Leaves oval-triangular to lanceolate; green-olive; unstalked; minutely toothed; often lengthwise folded; densely set. Flowers in tiny few-flowered heads not spikes.

> *Groenlandia densa*
> Opposite-leaved
> Pondweed

17 (13) **a** Leaves in **whorls** round stems. ——————————▶ 18
     b Leaves not in whorls; finely dissected. Flowers white and
      buttercup-like. ——————————————▶ 21

18 (17) **a** Leaves **simple**; in whorls of three (sometimes
     four); **oblong-oval**. Leaves up to 1 cm long; more
     or less blunt; dark green; translucent; bearing
     minute untoothed green scales on upper side near
     base. Female flowers 5 mm across; floating at
     surface on very long, thread-like stalks.

> *Elodea canadensis*
> Canadian Pondweed

     b Leaves and plant of other form. ——————————▶ 19

19 (18) **a** Leaves many; stiff; **linear**; forked at tips.
     Leaves rigid; dark green. Stems slender;
     20–100 cm long. Flowers small, solitary; in
     leaf-axils.

close-up of
leaf tips

> *Ceratophyllum*
> *demersum*
> Rigid Hornwort

     b Leaves **pinnately divided**, appearing feathery. ——————▶ 20

20 (19) **a** Usually four leaves to a whorl; finely pinnate into bristle-like segments. Flowers tiny; whorled; in spikes in leaf-axils; emerge from water.

> *Myriophyllum spicatum*
> Spiked Water Milfoil

b Usually three or four leaves in a whorl; more slender than **a**. Upper flowers alternate (not whorled) in short spikes in axils of tiny bracts. Petals yellow and red-streaked.

Flowers

> *Myriophyllum*
> *alterniflorum*
> Alternate-flowered
> Water Milfoil

c Similar to **b** but leaves larger and usually in whorls of five. Flowers in whorls in axils of pinnate leaf-like bracts.

> *Myriophyllum*
> *verticillatum*
> Whorled Water Milfoil

21 (17) **a** Leaves in **one plane**; **circular** in outline. Segments short and rigid. Like the spokes of a bicycle wheel with no rim. Flowers five-petalled; stamens exceeding head of achenes. Found in ditches, canals and slow streams.

> *Ranunculus circinatus*
> Stiff-leaved Water
> Crowfoot

leaf, showing segments

b Leaves not in one plane. ⟶ 22

22 (21) **a** Leaves **short**; 2–3 cm long; sessile or short-stalked; segments rigid. Flowers five-petalled; less than 6 mm long; achenes hairy. Variable plant of ponds, ditches and slow streams.

Ranunculus trichophyllus Short-leaved Water Crowfoot

leaf, showing segments

b Plant **large** and **robust** with creeping rhizomes. Leaves 8–30 cm long; greenish black with a few, very long, firm, slender, sub-parallel, occasionally forked, segments. Flowers 2–3 cm in diameter; petals, five to ten. Found in rapidly flowing streams and rivers.

Ranunculus fluitans Long-leaved Water Crowfoot

leaf, showing segments

SECTION C

1 a Aerial leaves **long-stalked; arrow-shaped.**
Submerged leaves linear; translucent. Floating
leaves oval-lanceolate. Inflorescence a simple,
erect, whorled raceme, 30–80 cm tall. Flowers 2 cm
or more across; 3–5 per whorl. Petals white with
purple spot at bases.

| *Sagittaria sagittifolia* |
| Arrowhead |

aerial leaf   part of
inflorescence

  b Leaves of other shape. ———————————————▶ 2

2 (1) a Leaves 2–4 cm across; **circular**; like tiny umbrellas.
Leaves hairless; edges scalloped; held erect; 1–15 cm
tall. Plant stem creeping and rooting.

| *Hydrocotyle vulgaris* |
| Marsh Pennywort |

  b Leaves of other shape and arrangement. ————————▶ 3

3 (2) a Leaves **basal**; may be very large. ——————————▶ 4
  b Leaves arranged along stems. ——————————————▶ 7

4 (3) a Leaves in **basal rosettes**; long-stalked; untoothed; parallel veined; more
or less erect. ————————————————————————▶ 5
  b Leaves basal; large; 10 cm or considerably more across; rather
rhubarb-like. ————————————————————————▶ 6

5 (4) **a** Leaves 8–20 cm long; **oval**; **pointed**; **rounded at base**. Inflorescence of several tiers of whorled branches which again branch into whorls. Flowers three-petalled; pinkish; in a flat, single whorl. Found on mud, in and by freshwater.

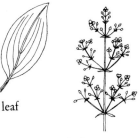

leaf

inflorescence

> *Alisma plantago-aquatica*
> Common Water Plantain

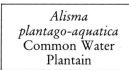

b Differs from **a** only in its **narrow lanceolate leaves** tapering to a stalk. Found in ponds etc.

leaf

> *Alisma lanceolatum*
> Narrow-leaved Water Plantain

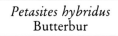

6 (4) **a** Leaves appear after flowers; long-stalked; distinctly toothed; **deeply heart-shaped** (in summer). May exceed 60 cm across. Flower-heads of reddish-pink tubular florets in stout-stalked racemes; 10–40 cm tall (in spring). Stream sides, wet places. (*Do not confuse with other imported exotic plants.*)

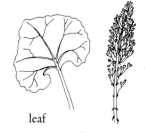

leaf

inflorescence

> *Petasites hybridus*
> Butterbur

b Plant more slender than **a**. Leaves appearing with flowers (in winter); **rounded, kidney- or heart-shaped**; 10–20 cm across. Flower-heads, few; lilac, vanilla-scented florets in racemes; 10–25 cm tall.

leaf

> *Petasites fragrans*
> Winter Heliotrope

7 (3) **a** Leaves **alternate.** ──────────────▶ 8
     b Leaves of other arrangement. ──────────▶ 16

8 (7) **a** **Membranous stipules** on stems at leaf-bases. ────▶ 9
     b Leaves without stipules at bases. ──────────▶ 13

9 (8) **a** Plant with violet-like flowers; pale lilac petals with deep blue veins. Flower-spur blunt. Plant low, creeping, with runners bearing long-stalked, hairless **kidney-shaped** leaves, up to 4 cm across.

> *Viola palustris*
> Marsh Violet

     b Plant **very large,** up to 2 m tall; **dock-like.** Inflorescence much branched. Leaves lanceolate-oval; pointed; up to 100 cm long. Inflorescence erect, with crowded whorls of tiny flowers. Found in shallow water, ditches, river sides etc.

flowers in whorls

> *Rumex hydrolapathum*
> Water Dock

     c Plant less than 1 m tall. Inflorescences usually unbranched; terminal or in leaf-axils. ──────────────────────▶ 10

10 (9) **a** Leaves with **black blotches.** ──────────────▶ 11
      b Leaves without black blotches. ─────────────▶ 12

11 (10) **a** Leaves lanceolate; 5–10 cm long. Stems up to 70 cm tall; reddish; swollen above leaf-bases; more or less erect and hairless. Stipules fringed. Inflorescences stout, blunt; flowers pink. Found in wet places.

inflorescence

> *Polygonum persicaria*
> Redshank

b Similar to **a** but larger; slightly hairy. Inflorescences stouter; flowers normally greenish white. Found in wet places.

> *Polygonum lapathifolium*
> Pale Persicaria

12 (10) **a** Leaves thin; lanceolate; 5–10 cm long. Stipules hardly fringed. More or less erect; hairless; up to 70 cm tall. Inflorescences slender; pointed; nodding and leafy below. Flowers pinkish or greenish white. Peppery taste. Found in shallow water and wet places.

> *Polygonum hydropiper*
> Water Pepper

b Similar to **a** but inflorescences more slender; fewer flowered; more pointed and drooping. Leaves rather abruptly narrowed at base. Stipules coarsely fringed. Flowers pink; 3–4 mm long. Not hot to taste.

> *Polygonum mite*
> Tasteless Water Pepper

c Leaves oval to oblong-lanceolate; blunt or pointed; base rounded. Plant more or less erect; 30–70 cm tall. Inflorescences 2–4 cm long; dense; many-flowered; terminal. Flowers pink; 2–3 mm long. Found in freshwater, on banks.

> *Polygonum amphibium*
> Amphibious Bistort

13 (8) **a** Leaves **oblong; downy hairy**; two or three times as long as wide. Plant creeping; 15–30 cm tall, with runners. Flowers with wheel-shaped, bright blue corollas with yellow eye; 8–10 mm wide. Found in marshes, ponds and streams.

> *Myosotis scorpioides*
> Water Forget-me-not

b Leaves of other shape; **hairless**. Flowers **buttercup-like; yellow.** ─────────────────────────────▶ 14

14 (13) **a** Leaves **heart-** or **kidney-shaped**; up to 10 cm across. Plant stout; stems hollow. Leaves up to 10 cm across; long-stalked below. Flowers 15–50 mm across; five yellow, petal-like sepals. No true petals; many yellow stamens. Found by rivers and wet areas.

leaf   flower

> *Caltha palustris*
> Marsh Marigold

b Leaves **lanceolate.** ─────────────────────────────▶ 15

15 (14) **a** Root leaves oblong; stalked. Stems hollow. Flowers few; 8–20 mm across. Flower-stalks **furrowed**. Sepals yellowish; petals yellow. Fruits in globular heads. Found in wet mud by ponds etc.

> *Ranunculus flammula*
> Lesser Spearwort

b Resembles **a** but taller (50–100 cm tall) and stouter. Stem-leaves up to 25 cm long. Flower-stalks **unfurrowed**. Flowers brighter yellow; 2–5 cm across.

> *Ranunculus lingua*
> Greater Spearwort

16 (7) **a** Leaves of variable arrangement; lower leaves opposite or in whorls of three; upper leaves alternate. Leaves sessile; oval-lanceolate; pointed; untoothed. Plant downy; erect; 60–120 cm tall. Inflorescence spike-like; dense; 10–30 cm long. Flowers in whorls, with 6 red-purple petals. Found by rivers, lakes, ponds etc.

flower

> *Lythrum salicaria*
> Purple Loosestrife

b Leaves in whorls. —————————————▶ 17
c Leaves opposite. ————————————————▶ 18

17 (16) **a** Leaves in whorls of three; oval; stalked; red toothed. Stems reddish; 1–2 m tall. Flowers in spikes; purplish pink (or white); snapdragon-like with short curved spurs. Found on river banks.

> *Impatiens glandulifera*
> Indian Balsam

b Leaves in whorls of four, five or six; stems four-angled. Leaves lanceolate; more or less blunt; broadest above middle; 3–5 cm long. Backward-pointing prickles on margins. Flowers 3–4.5 mm across; white. Plant variable with creeping and erect stems.

> *Galium palustre*
> Common Marsh
> Bedstraw

close-up of leaves

18 (16) **a** Leaves **untoothed**. ————————————▶ 19
b Leaves **toothed** (may be shallow). ——————▶ 22

19 (18) **a** Plant **tiny**; hairless; **creeping and rooting**. Leaves short-stalked; oval or near circular; 5 mm long. Stems delicate. Flowers in leaf-axils on stalks 1 cm long; corolla funnel-shaped; five-lobed; white with fine crimson veins, giving the flower a pink colour. Found in fens and wet meadows, often near the coast.

close-up of inflorescence

> *Anagallis tenella*
> Bog Pimpernel

b Plant without the combined features of the above. ————▶ 20

20 (19) **a** Leaves **linear** or **narrow lanceolate**; hairless. Leaves often waxy-grey. Flower-shoots 30–70 cm tall; rough; slightly hairy above. Flowers numerous; long-stalked; 3–4 cm across; petals deep rose-red; usually divided into four very narrow lobes. Found in moist meadows and fens.

> *Lychnis flos-cuculi*
> Ragged Robin

b Upper pairs of leaves close-set forming a flat, terminal rosette. ——————————————▶ 21

21 (20) **a** Leaves more or less **oval**; tip **shallow notched**; rosettes usually present. Roots arise from base of leaf pairs. Found in water, on wet mud etc.

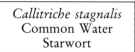

leaf

> *Callitriche stagnalis*
> Common Water Starwort

b Lower leaves **linear** with **deeply notched** spanner-shaped tips. Upper leaves may be spoon-shaped or elliptical or all leaves may be linear and parallel sided. Found in water, on wet mud etc.

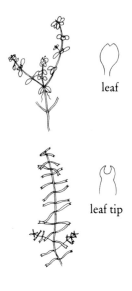

leaf tip

> *Callitriche intermedia*
> Intermediate Water Starwort

22 (18) **a** Stems **four-angled**. ━━━━━━━━━━━━━➤ 23
     b Stems not four-angled. ━━━━━━━━━━➤ 27

23 (22) **a Corners of stems winged**; flowers **snapdragon-like**. Leaves oval; blunt tipped; coarse toothed. Plant 40–80 cm tall; erect. Flowers with five sepals; corolla with two red-brown upper and three green lower lobes. Found in marshes and by water.

> *Scrophularia aquatica*
> Water Figwort

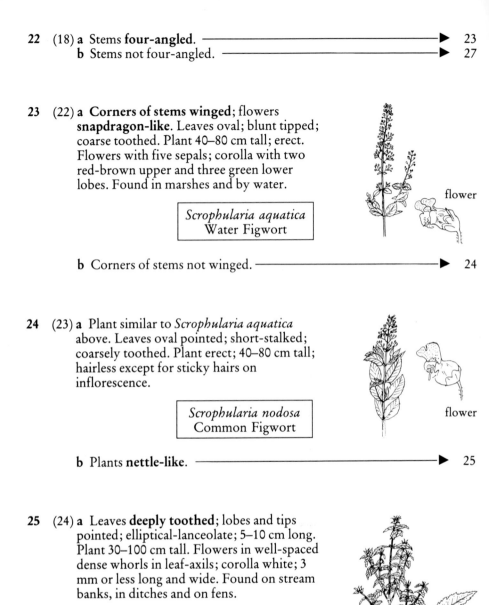

flower

     b Corners of stems not winged. ━━━━━━━━➤ 24

24 (23) **a** Plant similar to *Scrophularia aquatica* above. Leaves oval pointed; short-stalked; coarsely toothed. Plant erect; 40–80 cm tall; hairless except for sticky hairs on inflorescence.

> *Scrophularia nodosa*
> Common Figwort

flower

     b Plants **nettle-like**. ━━━━━━━━━━━━━➤ 25

25 (24) **a** Leaves **deeply toothed**; lobes and tips pointed; elliptical-lanceolate; 5–10 cm long. Plant 30–100 cm tall. Flowers in well-spaced dense whorls in leaf-axils; corolla white; 3 mm or less long and wide. Found on stream banks, in ditches and on fens.

> *Lycopus europaeus*
> Gipsywort

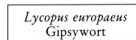

leaf

     b Leaves **more shallowly toothed**. ━━━━━━➤ 26

26 (25) a Leaves **oval**; more or less hairy with blunt tips and teeth. Plant 15–60 cm tall. Inflorescences rounded heads up to 2 cm long. Flowers with mauve corollas and stamens projecting from flowers. **Mint scented**. Found in marshes, fens and by water.

leaf

> *Mentha aquatica*
> Water Mint

b Leaves **lanceolate or oblong**; 5–12 cm long; short-stalked below; stalkless above. Plant 30–80 cm tall; erect. Inflorescence spike-like; flowers pink-purple with white pattern on lip. Found on marshes and stream sides.

> *Stachys palustris*
> Marsh Woundwort

27 (22) a Leaves **oval, toothed**; 2–7 cm long; upper leaves clasping stem. Flowers **snapdragon-like**; in axils of leaves and bracts; a raceme. Flowers 4–5 cm across; corolla with red spots in throat. Plant erect and creeping; 20–50 cm tall.

> *Mimulus guttatus*
> Monkey Flower

b Leaves **lanceolate or strap-shaped**; plants hairy. Flowers four-petalled; some shade of pink. ⟶ 28
c Leaves **shallow toothed**. Flower corolla **flat**; four-lobed; white or some shade of pink. ⟶ 30

28 (27) **a** Leaves **clasping**; lanceolate; pointed;
stalkless. Plant 80–150 cm tall with long
spreading hairs. Flowers purple-pink; 15–23
mm across; stigma with four stout creamy
lobes arched back. Found on fens, marshes
and river banks.

> *Epilobium hirsutum*
> Great Willowherb

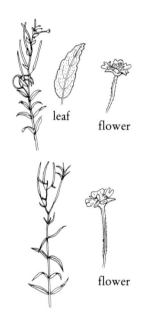

stigma

flower

leaf

b Leaves not clasping. ————————————➤ 29

29 (28) **a** Similar to *Epilobium hirsutum* but
shorter; 30–60 cm tall; less stout. Flowers
only 6–9 mm across; petals **pale pink**.
Found on marshes and stream sides.

> *Epilobium parviflorum*
> Hoary Willowherb

leaf

flower

b Leaves **stalkless**; **strap-shaped**; narrowed
at apex and base. Plant slender; 15–60 cm
tall. Flowers small; 4–6 mm across; stigma
undivided; club-shaped. Found in acid
marshes, bogs and ditches.

> *Epilobium palustre*
> Marsh Willowherb

flower

30 (27) **a** Leaves **oval; blunt; short stalked**; 3–6 cm long.
Stems fleshy; creeping and ascending; 20–60 cm
long. Inflorescence loose; many-flowered racemes
in axils of both of the pairs of leaves; corollas 7–8
mm wide, blue. Found in marshes, ponds and
ditches.

> *Veronica beccabunga*
> Brooklime;
> Water Speedwell

b Leaves **linear** or **oval-lanceolate**. ──────────▶ 31

31 (30) **a** Leaves **linear-lanceolate**; 2–4 cm long; **pointed**;
distinctly toothed; yellow-green or purplish. Plant
creeping and ascending; 10–50 cm long.
Inflorescences open; few-flowered racemes in axils
of only one of the pairs of leaves. Flower corollas
white or pale blue with purple veins. Found in
bogs, ponds and wet meadows.

> *Veronica scutellata*
> Marsh Speedwell

b More robust than *Veronica scutellata*. Leaves
oval-lanceolate, pointed, clasping, distinctly
toothed; 5–12 cm long. Stems fleshy; creeping and
ascending; up to 30 cm tall. Inflorescences many-
flowered racemes in axils of both of the pairs of
leaves. Flower-stalks equalling or longer than linear
bracts; corollas 5–6 mm wide; pale blue.

> *Veronica*
> *anagallis-aquatica*
> Blue Water Speedwell

SECTION D

1 **a** Leaves **pinnatifid.** ━━━━━━━━━━━━━━━━━━━━━━━━▶ 2
   b Leaves **compound.** ━━━━━━━━━━━━━━━━━━━━━━━━▶ 3

2 (1) **a** Stem leaves **opposite**; root-leaves long-stalked, undivided. Root-leaves oval-elliptical; 2–3 cm long. Stem-leaves more or less stalkless. Plant 15–30 cm tall with creeping runners at base. Inflorescences in terminal heads with tiny, pinkish flowers. Found in fen and wet meadows.

stem-leaf

> *Valeriana dioica*
> Marsh Valerian

b Stem-leaves **alternate**; root-leaves undivided. Root-leaves oval-elliptical; stem-leaves with large oval end-lobes. Inflorescences spreading and loosely branched; of large golden-yellow, **daisy-like** flowers; 25–30 mm across. Found in marshes and wet meadows.

stem-leaf

> *Senecio aquaticus*
> Marsh Ragwort

3 (1) **a** **Tiny leaflets alternate with larger leaflets.** Lower leaves stalked; **1-pinnate**; 30–60 cm long. 2–5 pairs of main leaflets; oval pointed; sharp toothed; white-woolly or downy below; leafy stipules at bases. Flowers creamy; fragrant; in dense irregular umbel-like inflorescences. Found by rivers, swamps and ditches.

> *Filipendula ulmaria*
> Meadowsweet

leaf

b Leaves in other arrangement. ━━━━━━━━━━━━━━━━▶ 4

4 (3) **a** Upper leaves **palmate** or **trifoliate**; lower leaves 1-**pinnate** with 5–7 leaflets. Plant up to 45 cm tall. Flowers in loose terminal cymes with five purplish sepals longer and wider than the five purple petals. Found in marshes and wet pools.

> *Potentilla palustris*
> Marsh Cinquefoil

    b Leaves either palmately lobed, trifoliate or variously pinnate. ──▶ 5

5 (4) **a** Leaves **palmately three-lobed**, long-stalked; shiny. Stem-leaves short-stalked; more divided. Stems short; stout; 20–60 cm tall. Flowers **buttercup-like**; shiny pale yellow in much-branched inflorescence. Found in mud by ditches, ponds etc.

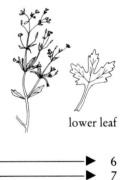

lower leaf

> *Ranunculus sceleratus*
> Celery-leaved Buttercup

    b Leaves **trifoliate**. ───────────────────────▶ 6
    c Leaves 1–4 times **pinnate**. ──────────────────▶ 7

6 (5) **a** Leaves **alternate**; long-stalked with **oval, untoothed,** grey-green leaflets; 3–7 cm long. Flower-stems leafless to 30 cm tall. Inflorescence a raceme of star-shaped flowers; pink outside; white inside; corolla of five lobes. Found in wet bogs and fens.

flower

Menyanthes trifoliata Bogbean

b Leaves **opposite**; hairy; stem leaves of three (sometimes five) **elliptical-lanceolate, toothed** leaflets; 5–10 cm long. Flowers of five or six reddish-pink tubular florets in large, rounded, much-branched panicles. Plant up to 120 cm tall. Found in marshes and fens.

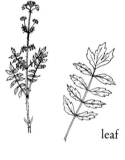

leaf

Eupatorium cannabinum Hemp Agrimony

7 (5) **a** Leaves **1-pinnate.** ──────────▶ 8
   b Leaves **2–4 times pinnate**; flowers in umbels. ──────▶ 14

8 (7) **a** Leaves **opposite**; up to 20 cm long; lower leaves long-stalked; leaflets lanceolate; more or less bluntly toothed; side veins conspicuous. Plant 30–120 cm tall; hairy below. Inflorescence terminal; umbel-like; funnel-shaped pinkish-white flowers. Found in fens, wet woods, riversides etc.

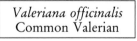

leaf

Valeriana officinalis Common Valerian

   b Leaves **alternate.** ──────────────▶ 9

9 (8) **a** Flowers in **umbels.** ──────────────▶ 10
   b Flowers not in umbels; leaves alternate. ──────▶ 13

10 (9) **a** Leaflets of aerial leaves **linear to narrow**; lobed. Submerged leaves with **deeply pinnatifid**, hair-like leaflets. Plant 10–50 cm long; often submerged or floating. Umbels 1–2 cm wide in leaf-axils, on stalks 1–3 cm long. Found in shallow ponds.

> *Apium inundatum*
> Lesser Marshwort

b Leaves 1- (sometimes 2-) **pinnate**; leaflets of lower leaves **oval-lobed**; upper leaflets **linear**, untoothed. Leaf-stalks longer than blades. Plant slender; 30–60 cm tall. Stems hollow; inflated at leaf junctions. Umbels few-rayed, forming dense balls. Found in marshes and pond edges.

> *Oenanthe fistulosa*
> Tubular Water
> Dropwort

c Leaves with **oval** or **oval-oblong, toothed** leaflets. ——————▶ 11

11 (10) **a** Leaves with 7–10 pairs of **oval leaflets**, quite deeply cut, each 2–5 cm long; dull bluish green. Plant 30–100 cm tall. Umbels 3–6 cm wide; short-stalked. Found in fens, ditches and ponds.

> *Berula erecta*
> Lesser Water Parsnip

leaf

b Leaves **alternate**. ————————————————▶ 12

12 (11) **a** Leaves up to 30 cm long; long-stalked. Leaflets **oval to oblong; toothed**; 2–15 cm long. Leaf-stalks hollow, sheathing stem. Plant robust; stem ridged; up to 2 m tall. Umbels 6–10 cm wide; terminal; flat topped; long-stalked. Found in fens, marshes, ditches etc.

leaf

> *Sium latifolium*
> Greater Water Parsnip

b Leaflets **shallowly, bluntly toothed; oval**; bright-green; shining. Plant creeping with ascending flower-stems; up to 80 cm tall. Umbels sessile or short-stalked, in leaf-axils. Found in fens, ditches and ponds.

> *Apium nodiflorum*
> Fool's Water Cress

13 (9) **a** Basal leaves in a rosette; long-stalked; terminal leaflet **kidney-shaped** and much larger than rounded laterals. Upper leaves with narrow leaflets. Plant erect or ascending; 30–60 cm tall; with runners. Flowers four-petalled; rose-pink to white; 12–18 mm across.

> *Cardamine pratensis*
> Lady's Smock

lower leaf

b Basal leaves stalked, of 5–9 oval leaflets; terminal leaflet largest. Upper leaflets 5–11; **oval to lanceolate**. Stems 10–60 cm tall; angled. Flowers white; 12 mm across; conspicuous **violet anthers**.

lower leaf

> *Cardamine amara*
> Large Bitter Cress

c Leaves similar to those of *Cardamine amara* but **darker green** and with **broader leaflets** below. Margins entire or wavy-toothed. Plant with creeping stems and erect flowering shoots. Flowers white; 2–4 mm across; **pale stamens**. Found in streams, ditches etc.

> *Rorippa*
> *nasturtium-aquaticum*
> Water Cress

14 *(7)* **a** Leaves **triangular**; 3–4 times pinnate; leaflets **oval**; bases tapered to stalk with several deep teeth above; leaf-stalks sheathing stem. Robust; hairless; stems hollow, grooved; up to 150 cm tall. VERY POISONOUS. Umbels stalked; terminal; 5–10 cm across. Found in marshes and ditches.

leaf

> *Oenanthe crocata*
> Hemlock Water
> Dropwort

b Leaves 3-pinnate; leaflets **hair-like** on submerged leaves; **lanceolate**; finely toothed on aerial leaves. Plant rather bushy; 30–100 cm tall with runners. Stems **very swollen** in lower part; 3–4 cm thick; hollow; very finely ridged. Umbels short-stalked; terminal and in leaf-axils. Found in ponds and ditches.

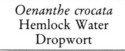

leaf

> *Oenanthe aquatica*
> Fine-leaved Water
> Dropwort

Bibliography

Clapham, A.R., Tutin, T.G. and Warburg, E.F. (1981). *Excursion Flora of the British Isles* (3rd edn.). Cambridge University Press.

Fitter, R., Fitter, A. and Farrer, A. (1984). *Guides to the Grasses, Sedges, Rushes and Ferns of Britain and Northern Europe*. Collins, London.

Haslam, S.M., Sinker, C.A. and Wolseley, P.A. (1975). British water plants. *Field Studies*, 4, pp. 243–351.

Hubbard, C.E. (1984). *Grasses* (3rd edn.). Penguin Books, London.

Jermy, A.C., Chater, A.O. and David, R.W. (1982). *Sedges of the British Isles*. Botanical Society of the British Isles.

McClintock, D. and Fitter, R.S.R. (1956). *Pocket Guide to Wild Flowers*. Collins, London.

Rose, F. (1981). *The Wild Flower Key*. Frederick Warne, London.

Index

Notes